S0-ARK-921

Hello, there! It's Hopsalot here, and my friends and I are preparing for our big adventure. We are going around the world in a hot air balloon! I hope you'll join us. This trip is going to be stupendous!

See these carrots? Every time you learn something new, you get one of these stickers to put in your basket. When you finish each section, you get a big flag sticker to put on your Certificate of Completion at the end of the book!

See this picture of me? When you see it, that means I am there to help you. Just look for **Hopsalot's Hints**.

Are you ready to take off? Here we go!

To put events in **order**, decide what happened first and what happened next.

We're getting ready for our hot air balloon adventure! **Look at the pictures below. Write a 1 under what happened first, and a 2 under what happened next.**

_ _ _ _ _ _ _ _

_ _ _ _ _ _ _ _

_ _ _ _ _ _ _ _

_ _ _ _ _ _ _ _

It's time for takeoff! **Write a 1 under the picture that shows what happened first. Write a 2 under the picture that shows what happened next.**

_____
- - - - - - -
_____

_____
- - - - - -
_____

Great job! Put your carrot sticker in your basket and jump ahead to the next level!

Here are some pictures of us getting ready for our trip. They're all mixed up! Help us put them in order. **Write 1, 2, and 3 near the pictures to show what happened first, next, and last.**

_____

- - - - - - -

_____

_____

- - - - - - -

_____

_____

- - - - - - -

_____

We decided to come down and go roller-skating!
Put the three pictures in order. Write 1, 2, or 3 near each picture to show what happened first, next, and last.

Here are some pictures of us eating dinner. We are at Grandpa's house on the bayou! **What happened first, next, and last? Write 1, 2, and 3 on the lines to show the correct order.**

Uh-oh! The basket has a hole in it! We need to get it fixed. I hear there's a bird mechanic around here. **Write 1, 2, and 3 on the lines to show the order in which things happened.**

_____
- - - - -
_____

_____
- - - - -
_____

Stupendous! Put your carrot sticker in your basket and jump ahead to the next level!

Sequencing 7

Hopsalot's Hints

When pictures or events are in the right order, they make a **sequence**.

We finally made it to Grandma's house up north. We baked a carrot cake together! **Write 1, 2, or 3 to show the order of these three steps. Then draw your own picture to show what you think will happen next.**

_ _ _ _ _ _ _ _

_ _ _ _ _ _ _ _

_ _ _ _ _ _ _ _

We were having so much fun at Grandma's, we decided to stay another day! Look at us bowling out on the ice. **Put the pictures in order. Write 1, 2, or 3 next to each picture and then draw what you think will happen next.**

 _ _ _ _ _ _ _

 _ _ _ _ _ _ _

 _ _ _ _ _ _ _

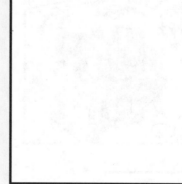

Excellent job! Put your carrot sticker in your basket and jump ahead!

Sequencing 9

Level 3

I need to go to five different places today. Help me go in the right order. **Write 1, 2, 3, 4, or 5 for every place I visit. Be sure to follow the directions!**

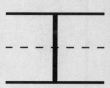

_____
- - - - - - - -
_____

_____
- - - - - - - -
_____

1. I need to go to the schoolhouse first.
2. I need to go to the grocery store second.
3. Take me to the basketball court third, please.
4. For my fourth stop, I need to go home and have dinner.
5. At last, it is time for me to go to bed. Good-night!

_ _ _
- - - - - - -
_ _ _

_ _ _
- - - - - - -

What do you think I will do first thing in the morning? Draw it here.

Great playing! Put your big flag sticker on the Certificate of Completion and jump ahead!

Review 11

Where should we go next? Roquefort has never been to the beach. Let's go! **Put an X on the things that we could do at the beach.**

What do you like to do at the beach or in a pool? On a separate piece of paper, draw a picture of it.

The big city is the place for Bebop! He wants to stop there next. **Put an X on the things that we might do in the city.**

Terrific job! Put your carrot sticker in your basket and jump ahead to the next level!

Storytelling Skills   **13**

Gee, my hair has really grown on this trip! **Look at the two pictures of me at the barbershop. Put an X on the picture that shows what happened first. Then color the picture of me after my haircut.**

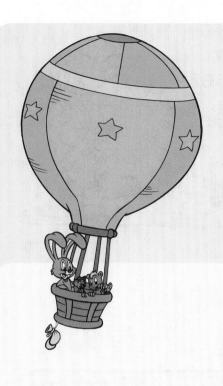

Look what we saw in the treetop! See this picture? **Draw what you think happened before it in the top box. Draw what you think happened after it in the bottom box.**

We decided to stop off to play soccer in Italy! **Write 1, 2, or 3 next to each picture to show what happened first, next, and last.**

_____
- - - - - - - - -
_____

_____
- - - - - - - - -
_____

_____
- - - - - - - - -
_____

Can you describe what happened in your own words?

Now we're visiting Gracie in Mexico.
We're helping her grow a tomato plant.
**Write 1, 2, or 3 near the pictures to show
what happened first, next, and last.
Then draw a picture of
Gracie's best tomato.**

_____
- - - - - - -
_____

_____
- - - - - - -
_____

_____
- - - - - -
_____

Hopsalot's Hints

You can ask a grown-up to help you write down your ideas and stories.

It's story time in the hot air balloon! **Read the story below. Then write down your wishes on the lines. Ask a grown-up to help you.**

Once upon a time, there was a fairy godmother. It was her job to give three wishes to anyone who asked. Now she's going to give **YOU** three wishes!

What are your three wishes?

I wish for _____

I wish for _____

I wish for _____

I am telling my friends a story.
Read the story and follow the directions below.

My 🦷 was loose.
    I wiggled it and wiggled it.
One day I bit into a  and it fell out!
My mom told me to put it under my 🛏.
    That night the 🦷 fairy came to visit me!
In the morning, I looked under my 🛏.
    What do you think she left me?

Write what you think the tooth fairy left for Hopsalot. On a separate piece of paper, draw a picture to go with what you wrote.

_____

- - - - - - - - - - - - - - - - - - -

_____

I made up my own fairy tale.

Once upon a time, there was a named Fred.

He had lost his way .

He hopped and hopped.

Then he met a named Bonnie.

What was the frog's name?

_____

- - - - - - - - - - - - - - - - -

_____

What was the bird's name?

_____

- - - - - - - - - - - - - - - - -

_____

Have an adult help you read the story and answer the questions below.

 flew high up in the . She saw

his  and told him where it was. Now

he knew how to get home. and

were friends forever.

What problem did the frog have?

_____

- -

_____

How did the bird help the frog?

_____

- -

_____

Stupendous! Put your big flag sticker on the Certificate of Completion and jump ahead!

Review **21**

Hopsalot's Hints

Songs can describe an idea or tell a story.

It's Jack's birthday! Let's all sing "Happy Birthday" to him. **Read the words and sing along. Look at the picture. Then answer the questions below.**

Happy Birthday to you,

Happy Birthday to you,

Happy Birthday, dear Jack,

Happy Birthday to you.

Whose birthday is it?
What did Jack have instead of a birthday cake?
When is your birthday?

Bebop taught Hopsalot a song to sing to the farmer. It is sung to the tune of "How Much Is That Doggie in the Window?" **Sing it out loud. Then answer the questions below.**

How much is that carrot in the basket?

The one with the really green tail?

How much is that carrot in the basket?

I do hope that carrot's for sale.

What is this song about?
Who taught Hopsalot to sing this song?
What color is the carrot's tail?

Bebop is reading us the beginning of a story. **Have a grown-up help you read the story. Then answer the questions below.**

The Three Billy Goats Gruff

Once upon a time, there were three billy 's.

They wanted to cross a  to have a

picnic on the other side, but there was a

living under the ! The said, "You

can't go over my !"

Where did the live?

What did the say to the 's?

If you were a , what would you say to

the so that he would let you cross the ?

This story is one of our favorites.
Read along with a grown-up.
Then answer the questions.

Goldilocks and the Three Bears

Papa Bear, Mama Bear, and Baby Bear went for a walk in the woods. A little girl named Goldilocks came into their 🏠. She ate their 🥣, sat in their 🪑🪑🪑, and rested in their 🛏🛏🛏. She fell asleep in Baby Bear's 🛏!

When the three bears came back, they said, "Who's been eating our 🥣 and sitting in our 🪑's and sleeping in our 🛏's?" Then, Goldilocks woke up and ran away.

Who was in the bear family?
What was the little girl's name?
What did the little girl do in the bears' 🏠?
What did she do when she got caught?

Read another story with us.
Answer the questions at the end.

Little Red Riding Hood

Once upon a time, 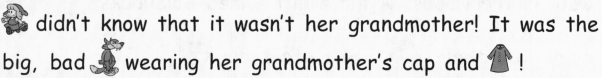 was going to her grandmother's 🏠.

When she got there her grandmother was in 🛏️.

👧 didn't know that it wasn't her grandmother! It was the

big, bad 🐺 wearing her grandmother's cap and 👘 !

"Grandmother, what big 👀 you have," said 👧.

"The better to see you with, my dear," said the 🐺.

"Grandmother, what big 👂 you have," said 👧.

"The better to hear you with, my dear," said the 🐺.

"Grandmother, what big 🦷 you have," said 👧.

"The better to eat you up!" said the 🐺.

👧 realized that it wasn't her grandmother at all! It was

a big, bad 🐺 !

How did 👧 get to her grandmother's 🏠 ?

Why do you think 👧 didn't know it was the 🐺 in

her grandmother's 🛏️ ?

Do you know what happens next in the story?

Here's another good story.
Read along and answer the questions below.

The Lion and the Mouse

Once upon a time, there was a and a 🐭 .

The wanted to eat the 🐭 !

The 🐭 said, "Please do not eat me! If you do not eat

me, I will be your friend."

The 🦁 said okay. Then the next day the got

caught in a . Someone was trying to catch him!

The 🐭 chewed through the 🥅 and the 🦁 escaped.

The 🐭 and the 🦁 were friends forever.

Why do you think the let the 🐭 go?

How did the 🐭 help the ?

What happens at the end of the story?

Great job! Put your carrot sticker in your basket and jump ahead to the next level!

Reading Comprehension (27)

Hopsalot's Hints

A **folktale** is a story that has been told for many, many years.

Here's another story. **Read along and answer the questions below.**

The Tortoise and the Hare

Once upon a time, there was a 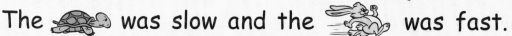 and a 🐰.
The 🐢 was slow and the 🐰 was fast.
One day, the 🐢 challenged the 🐰 to a race.
The 🐰 laughed at the 🐢 and said, "HA!
I will win."
The race began. The 🐢 went slow, but he tried hard. The 🐰 went fast, but he stopped to take a nap and eat a snack. He didn't even notice that the 🐢 had passed him! The 🐢 won the race!

Who was in the race?
Who did the 🐰 think would win the race?
Who won the race?

It's so much fun to make up stories. See these pictures? **Use them to make up your own story. What is happening in each picture? Ask a grown-up to write your story down on the lines below.**

_____

_____

_____

_____

_____

_____

Super storytelling! Put your carrot sticker in your basket and jump ahead.

What a fun trip that was.

Dear Diary,

I had so much fun on my trip! It was fun to

fly in the . I had fun being with my

friends, and . My three favorite things

about the trip were:

1. Going to 's house and bowling on the ice.

2. Playing with my friends.

Read Hopsalot's diary. Then answer the questions.

3. Reading  with my friends—my favorite

was the one about the  and the .

Well, it's time to fly back home. What a great trip!

Who is writing in his diary?

What were his three favorite things about this trip?

What was his favorite story?

Where is he going now?

Hooray! You did it! Put your big flag sticker on the Certificate of Completion!

Review (31)

Answer Key

PAGE 2	1, 2
PAGE 3	2, 1
PAGE 4	3, 2, 1
PAGE 5	3, 2, 1
PAGE 6	1, 3, 2
PAGE 7	3, 2, 1
PAGE 8	3, 2, 1
PAGE 9	1, 2, 3
PAGES 10–11	1, 5, 2, 4, 3; answers will vary
PAGE 12	beach scenes X'd
PAGE 13	city scenes X'd
PAGE 14	picture on left X'd drawings will vary
PAGE 15	first box should show an unhatched bird's egg; last box should show a baby bird fully hatched
PAGE 16	1, 2, 3; answers will vary
PAGE 17	1, 3, 2; drawings will vary
PAGE 18	answers will vary
PAGE 19	answers will vary
PAGES 20–21	Fred; Bonnie; Fred was lost; the bird helped him find his way
PAGE 22	Jack's; cheese; answers will vary
PAGE 23	wanting a carrot; Bebop; answers will vary
PAGE 24	under the bridge; "You can't go over my bridge!"; answers will vary

PAGE 25	Papa Bear, Mama Bear, Baby Bear; Goldilocks; ate their soup, sat in their chairs, rested in their beds; ran away
PAGE 26	she walked through the woods; answers will vary
PAGE 27	answers will vary; the mouse gnawed through the net; they became friends
PAGE 28	tortoise and hare; himself; tortoise
PAGE 29	answers will vary
PAGES 30–31	Hopsalot; bowling on ice at Grandma's house, playing soccer, reading stories; The Tortoise and the Hare; home